SPIDER-MAN

£5.50
UK only

The Official Spider-Man Annual 1997

Based on the smash hit
animated series

Origination by Newsstand Services
Editor: **Peter Nicholls**
Design: **Rob Sharp**
Andrew Ridgway

Published in Great Britain by World
International Ltd., Deanway Technology
Centre, Wilmslow Road, Handforth,
Cheshire SK9 3FB

Printed in the United Kingdom

ISBN: 0 7498 2818 8

Contents

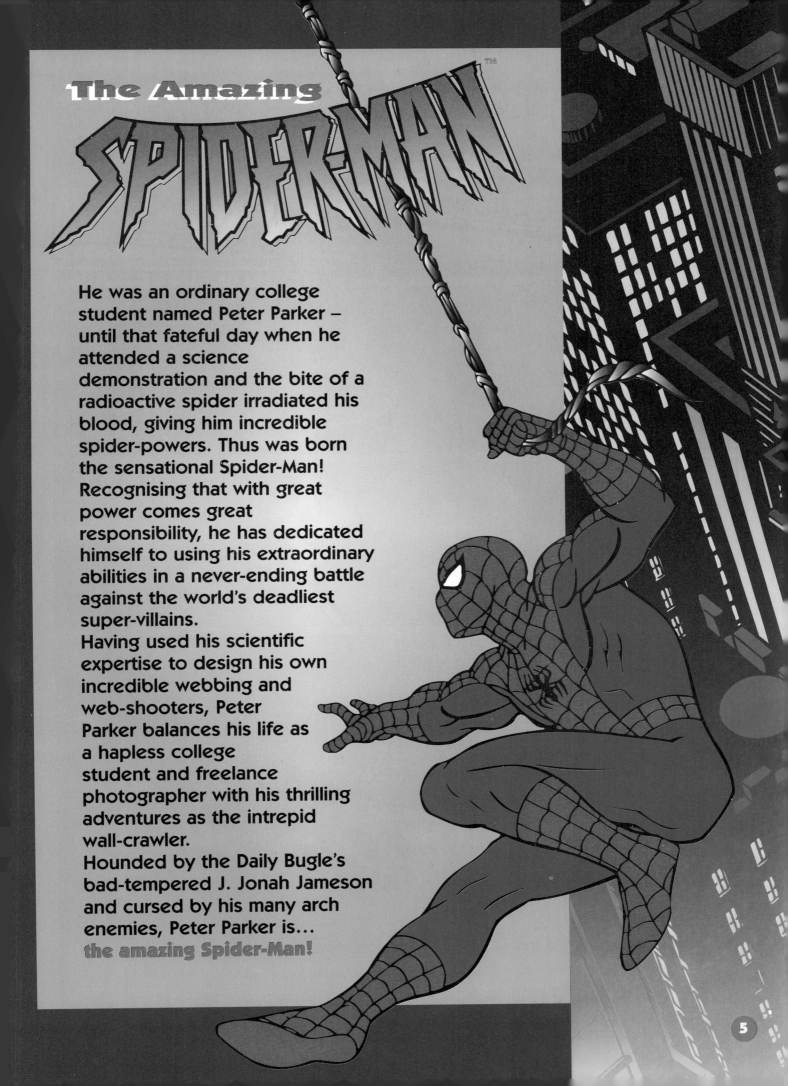

The Amazing SPIDER-MAN

He was an ordinary college student named Peter Parker – until that fateful day when he attended a science demonstration and the bite of a radioactive spider irradiated his blood, giving him incredible spider-powers. Thus was born the sensational Spider-Man! Recognising that with great power comes great responsibility, he has dedicated himself to using his extraordinary abilities in a never-ending battle against the world's deadliest super-villains.

Having used his scientific expertise to design his own incredible webbing and web-shooters, Peter Parker balances his life as a hapless college student and freelance photographer with his thrilling adventures as the intrepid wall-crawler.

Hounded by the Daily Bugle's bad-tempered J. Jonah Jameson and cursed by his many arch enemies, Peter Parker is... the amazing Spider-Man!

STUDENT *PETER PARKER* GAINED THE PROPORTIONATE STRENGTH AND AGILITY OF A SPIDER AFTER HE WAS BITTEN BY A RADIOACTIVE SPIDER. ARMED WITH WONDROUS WEB-SHOOTERS AND COMMITTED TO USING HIS AMAZING POWERS FOR GOOD, HE BATTLES SOME OF THE MOST SINISTER SUPER-VILLAINS ON EARTH AS A SUPER HERO WHILE STRUGGLING TO LEAD A NORMAL LIFE AS PETER!

ADAPTED FROM HIS ANIMATED TELEVISION SHOW, THE STORY WITHIN THESE PAGES IS THE LATEST AMAZING CHAPTER OF... SPIDER-MAN ADVENTURES

JOHN F. KENNEDY INTERNATIONAL AIRPORT, QUEENS, NEW YORK CITY...

...GATEWAY TO AMERICAN SHORES FOR THE THOUSANDS THAT LAND DAILY...

US CUSTOMS

...WHERE WORLD-WEARY TRAVELLERS ARE OFFERED A WARM, YET CAUTIOUS WELCOME...

THAT'S HIM. NO DOUBT ABOUT IT. GREEN SUIT'S OUR MAN. C'MON, LET'S MOVE IN.

NOT YET. HE DOESN'T SUSPECT--

OH! NO!

"--HE'S SPOTTED US!"

RUSH HIM!

UNGH!

YOU'RE TOO LATE, AGENTS!

KOFF *KOFF* SEAL THE EXITS IF HE GETS AWAY--

PHWOOM

ANOTHER *EXPLOSIVE* CHAPTER IN THE LIFE OF THE AMAZING SPIDER-MAN BROUGHT TO YOU BY:

NEL YOMTOV WRITER — ALEX SAVIUK PENCILER — ROB STULL INKER — STEVE DUTRO LETTERER — KEVIN TINSLEY COLOURIST — SARRA MOSSOFF EDITOR — BOB BUDIANSKY CHIEF

FREELY ADAPTED FROM A STORY AND SCREENPLAY BY JOHN SEMPER

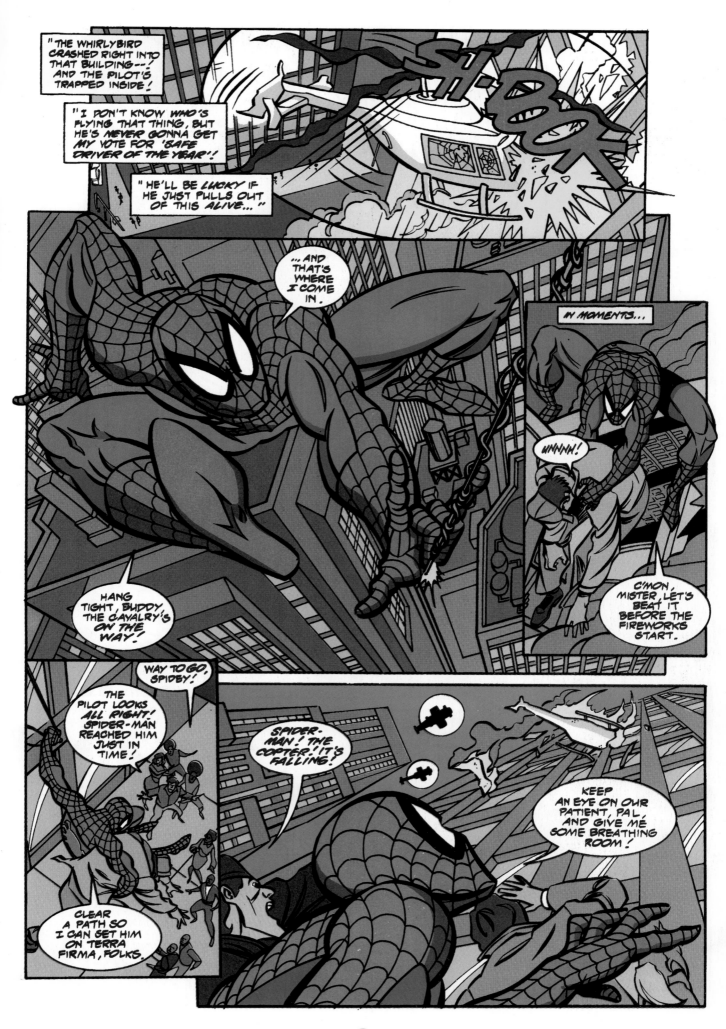

THINK ABOUT IT, MR. JAMESON...TWO WORLD LEADERS SIGNING A PEACE TREATY AFTER CENTURIES OF HOSTILE AGGRESSIONS...

...I COULD WIN A PULITZER PRIZE FOR THE BUGLE WITH JUST ONE GOOD SHOT.

SORRY, PARKER, EACH PAPER GETS ONLY ONE PHOTOGRAPHER AT THE SIGNING.

THEN HOW ABOUT YOUR PARTY TONIGHT? IT'LL BE THE ONLY TIME THEY'LL BE TOGETHER BEFORE THE SIGNING.

AFTER ALL THE GREAT SPIDER-MAN PHOTOS I'VE TAKEN--

ALL RIGHT, STOP IT ALREADY! YOU'RE BREAKING MY HEART!

I'LL SEE IF I CAN GET YOU CLEARANCE.

OH, THAT'S GREAT MR. JAMESON! YOU WON'T BE SORRY YOU GAVE ME THE CHANCE TO--

FINE, FINE. JUST SHUT UP, WILLYA?

HEY, DRIVER!

SHREE

THIS ISN'T ANYWHERE NEAR MY TAILOR! IF YOU THINK YOU'RE GOING TO SQUEEZE ME FOR A BIGGER FARE--

JUST BE CALM, MR. JAMESON. NO HARM WILL COME TO YOU.

NOW PLEASE SIT BACK.

SOUNDS SERIOUS, MR. JAMESON. WHAT DID YOU DO?

...FORGET TO PAY LAST MONTH'S TAILOR'S BILL?

GRAB YOUR ARMRESTS, GENTLEMEN...

MEANWHILE...

DAILY BUGLE

AT LAST! THE FILES OF "MY" TRUSTED STAFF...

PETER PARKER, FREELANCE PHOTOGRAPHER. ROBBIE ROBERTSON, EDITOR. GLORY GRANT, EXECUTIVE SECRETARY.

EXCELLENT AND USEFUL ADDITIONS TO MY BELT'S VIDEO RECEIVER...

MISTER JAMESON!

YOU'RE BACK EARLY. IS YOUR TUXEDO FITTING FINISHED ALREADY?

WELL, I NEED THEM IN MY HANDS RIGHT NOW.

DO YOU HAVE A PROBLEM WITH THAT?

YEAH, ALL DONE. NOW I NEED THE SECURITY PLANS FOR TONIGHT'S PARTY.

WHERE ARE THEY?

N-NO, SIR! I'LL GO--

AND GET ME ANOTHER SET! NOW!

I LEFT A COPY IN YOUR BRIEFCASE HALF AN HOUR AGO.

HMPH! WITH ALL THE EXTRA ORDERS HE GIVES ME, SOMETIMES I THINK THERE ARE TWO OF HIM!

COULD YOU IMAGINE A WORLD WITH TWO JONAH JAMESONS?

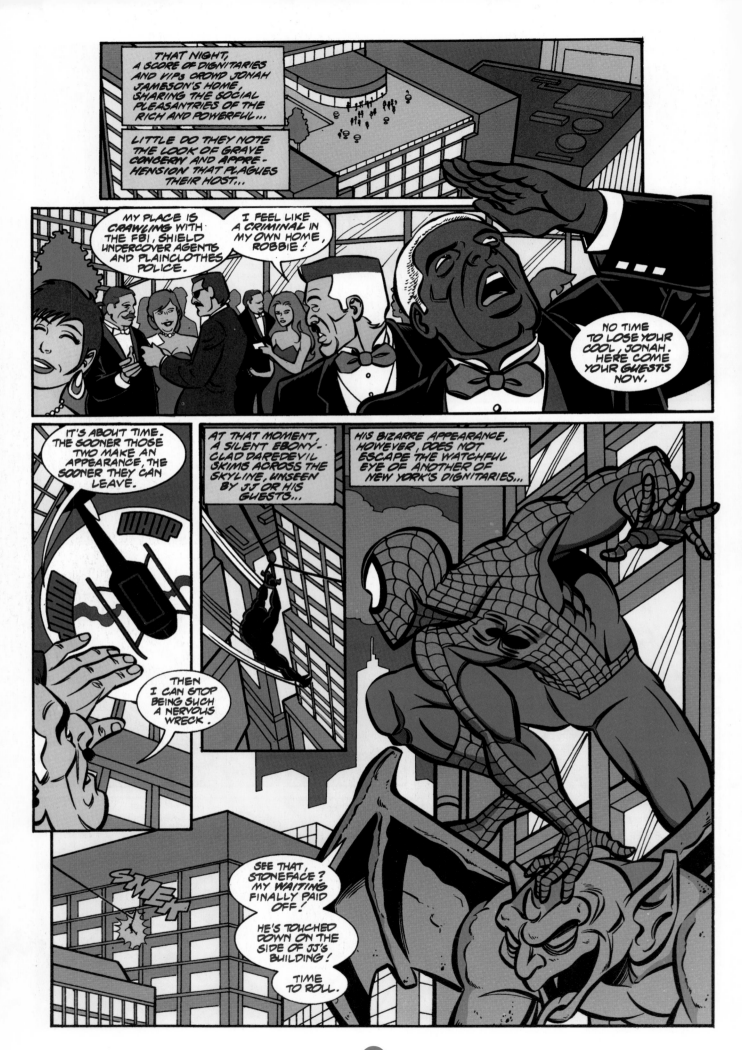

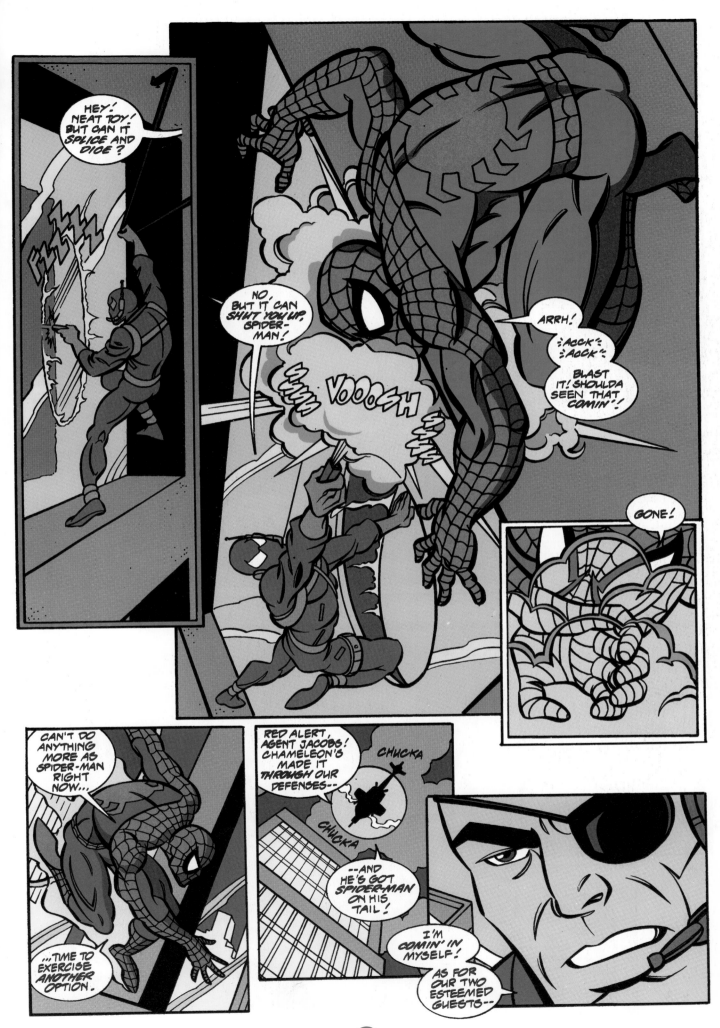

--GET THEM OUT NOW!

I HEARD THAT, AGENT. AND AS FAR AS I'M CONCERNED--

--IT'S GOOD NEWS TO ME!

NO SIGN OF CHAMELEON... WHOEVER HE LOOKS LIKE NOW. TIME TO CHECK THINGS OUTSIDE.

SORRY TO RUSH YOU AWAY FROM THE PARTY, GENTLEMEN, BUT YOU'VE GOT A LONG DAY TOMORROW.

WATCH YOUR STEP AND PLEASE HURRY.

GOOD. NOW CHAMELEON WILL NEVER GET A SHOT AT THEM...

COLONEL FURY? YOU'VE GOTTEN HERE QUICKLY, SIR.

HOW DID YOU--?

BUTTON IT UP AND LET ME TAKE OVER, AGENT!

I WILL PERSONALLY GET THESE TWO TO SAFETY!

LOOK AT THIS! FURY'S HERE IN THE FLESH! LET'S SEE HOW THE OLD WAR HERO HANDLES THIS ONE...

WAIT A MINUTE! OH, NO!

22

SORRY TO PUT AN END TO YOUR CAREER AS "ENQUIRING PHOTOGRAPHER"...

--BUT YOUR PAPARAZZI DAYS ARE OVER!

KRUNCH!

LET'S SEE HOW THAT GIZMO OF YOURS HOLDS UP TO THE SPIDEY STRESS TEST...!

AWWRH! NO! NOT THAT...!

IF NOT

FOR YOU

I WOULD

HAVE SUCCEEDED

SO CLOSE

I WAS SO CLOSE...

THE CHAMELEON? HERE? RIGHT NEXT TO ME?

OH, I DON'T FEEL SO GOOD...

FOR THE SAKE OF WORLD PEACE, JAMESON...

...TRY NOT TO GET SICK IN THE UNITED NATIONS!

SEE YA IN THE FUNNY PAPERS, GANG!

I NEED A VACATION... A NICE LONG VACATION.

SOME-WHERE WITH NO CHAMELEON. NO SPIDER-MAN. NO PARKER...

27

SPIDER-MAN

Fact File

SPIDER-MAN

SECRET IDENTITY: Peter Parker

HEIGHT: 5' 10"

FRIENDS AND FAMILY: Aunt May and Uncle Ben, who raised Peter after his parents died. Uncle Ben was shot by a thief who Spider-Man had earlier refused to stop. It was the death of his uncle which made Peter realise that with great power comes great responsibility. Peter's best friend is Harry Osborn, whose father is secretly Spider-Man's greatest enemy, the Green Goblin. Peter's girlfriend is Mary Jane Watson, a college student who hopes to be a model and actress.

ORIGIN: While attending a science demonstration at college, Peter gained his spider-powers after being bitten by a radioactive spider.

POWERS: Spider-Man has the proportionate strength and speed of a spider. He can stick to any surface, which gives him the ability to climb walls and cling to ceilings. His spider-sense tingles to warn him of any impending danger. He is extremely agile and has heightened reflexes.

COSTUME FEATURES: Spidey himself designed the mechanical web-shooters worn around his wrists. These enable him to shoot out lines of webbing which he uses to swing around town or trap his enemies. The webbing can be adjusted to produce a web net or a super-sticky liquid.
The eye-pieces in his mask are actually one-way lenses. He can see out but no-one can see in.
Hidden in his belt are the spider signal projector and his automatic camera which he uses to take photographs of the battles with his adversaries. As Peter Parker, he earns his living by selling these shots to The Daily Bugle's editor-in-chief, J. Jonah Jameson.

ENEMIES: There's a horde of malevolent super-villains determined to defeat Spider-Man, including Doctor Octopus, The Kingpin, Venom, Kraven the Hunter, the Green Goblin, The Shocker, Hobgoblin and lots more. Look out, Spidey!

THE CHAMELEON

REAL NAME: Unknown

OCCUPATION: Professional criminal

PLACE OF BIRTH: Unknown (possibly Soviet Union)

HEIGHT: Unknown

BASE OF OPERATIONS: Mobile

POWERS: The Chameleon is a brilliant master of disguise. He is highly skilled at creating lifelike masks and make-up. Due to a serum he ingested, his face is all but featureless. With the use of the electrical impulses in his belt, The Chameleon can completely reshape his skin into the features of virtually any human being. Before the skin on his face became so malleable, he was a talented quick-change artist who could assume a new disguise in less than a minute.

WEAPONS: The buckle on his belt contains a microcomputer programmed with the faces of thousands of people. It analyses facial characteristics and duplicates them, using electrical impulses. These characteristics can then be assumed by The Chameleon. The belt is also equipped with a hologram projector which The Chameleon uses for more complex disguises.

MYSTERIO

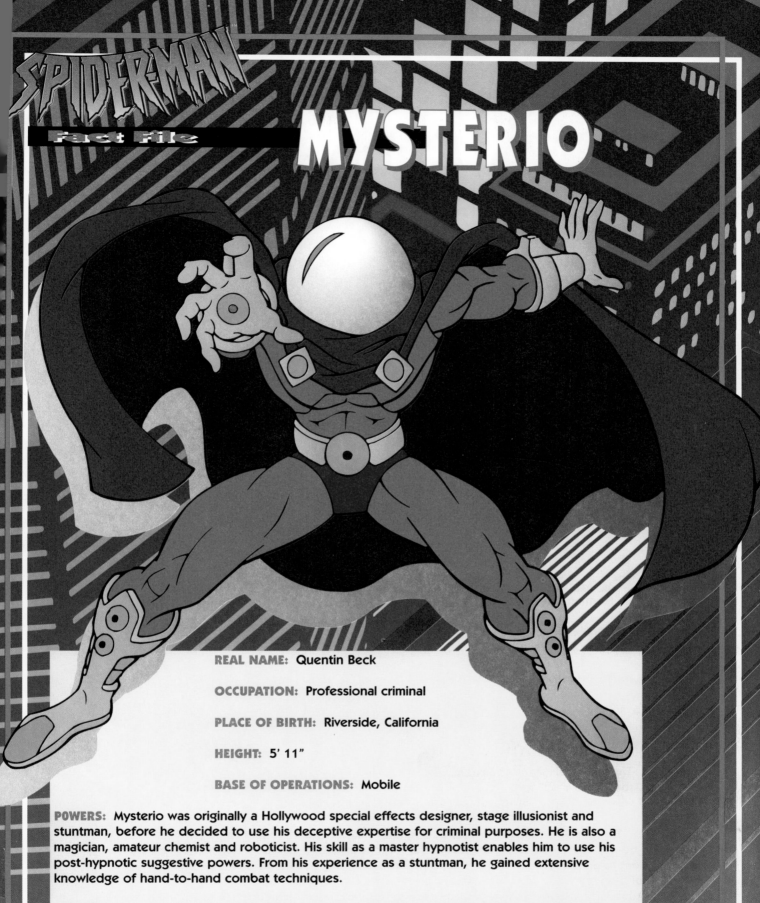

REAL NAME: Quentin Beck

OCCUPATION: Professional criminal

PLACE OF BIRTH: Riverside, California

HEIGHT: 5' 11"

BASE OF OPERATIONS: Mobile

POWERS: Mysterio was originally a Hollywood special effects designer, stage illusionist and stuntman, before he decided to use his deceptive expertise for criminal purposes. He is also a magician, amateur chemist and roboticist. His skill as a master hypnotist enables him to use his post-hypnotic suggestive powers. From his experience as a stuntman, he gained extensive knowledge of hand-to-hand combat techniques.

WEAPONS: Mysterio's distinctive helmet is made of one-way plexiglass and is equipped with a holographic projector. His costume is fashioned from a unique synthetic stretch fabric, while his gloves and boots are armed with nozzles which emit hallucinogenic gas. In addition, he carries conventional hand-held weapons and hypnotic aids.

SPIDER-MAN
Fact File
GREEN GOBLIN

REAL NAME: Norman Osborn

OCCUPATION: Professional criminal, owner and president of Oscorp

PLACE OF BIRTH: Hartford, Connecticut

HEIGHT: 5' 11"

BASE OF OPERATIONS: New York City

POWERS: The chemical that transformed Norman Osborn into the Green Goblin increased his strength, possibly to superhuman level, especially when he is enraged. It also gave him increased intelligence.

WEAPONS: The Green Goblin is a genius at inventing weaponry and concocting chemicals. His 'pumpkin bombs' are incendiary grenades in the form of miniature jack-o-lanterns. They release enough heat to melt through a 3-inch thick sheet of steel. The Goblin has created different varieties of bombs, designed to emit smoke and hallucinogenic gas.
His gloves are equipped to discharge bolts of high frequency electrical power. Rechargeable power packs are stored in the glove cuffs and costume tunic.
The Green Goblin's method of transportation is his goblin-glider, capable of great manoeuvrability and speeds of up to 90 miles per hour. He is also a brilliant criminal strategist.

VENOM

REAL NAME: Eddie Brock

OCCUPATION: Reporter (currently unemployed)   **PLACE OF BIRTH:** Unknown

HEIGHT: Unknown   **BASE OF OPERATIONS:** New York City

POWERS: Venom's costume is actually a living entity, an alien symbiote which bonded with disgraced ex-Daily Bugle reporter Eddie Brock. Originally, the alien had attached itself to Spider-Man. Before Spidey managed to free himself of the otherworldly being, it was able to mimic the wall-crawler's uncanny abilities. It retained these powers when it joined with Brock to become the sinister creature known as Venom, whose powers include superhuman strength, super-speed, the ability to climb walls and a spider-sense. He can also avoid Spider-Man's own spider-sense.

WEAPONS: Venom's whole body is his weapon! From Spider-Man, he has inherited the ability to produce and shoot his own version of Spider-Man's extraordinary webbing. Venom's only weakness appears to be his sensitivity to loud sounds. Eddie Brock's intense hatred of Spider-Man makes Venom one of the web-swinger's most obsessive and lethal foes.

Script: Glenn Dakin Art: Brian Williamson Lettering: Peter Nicholls

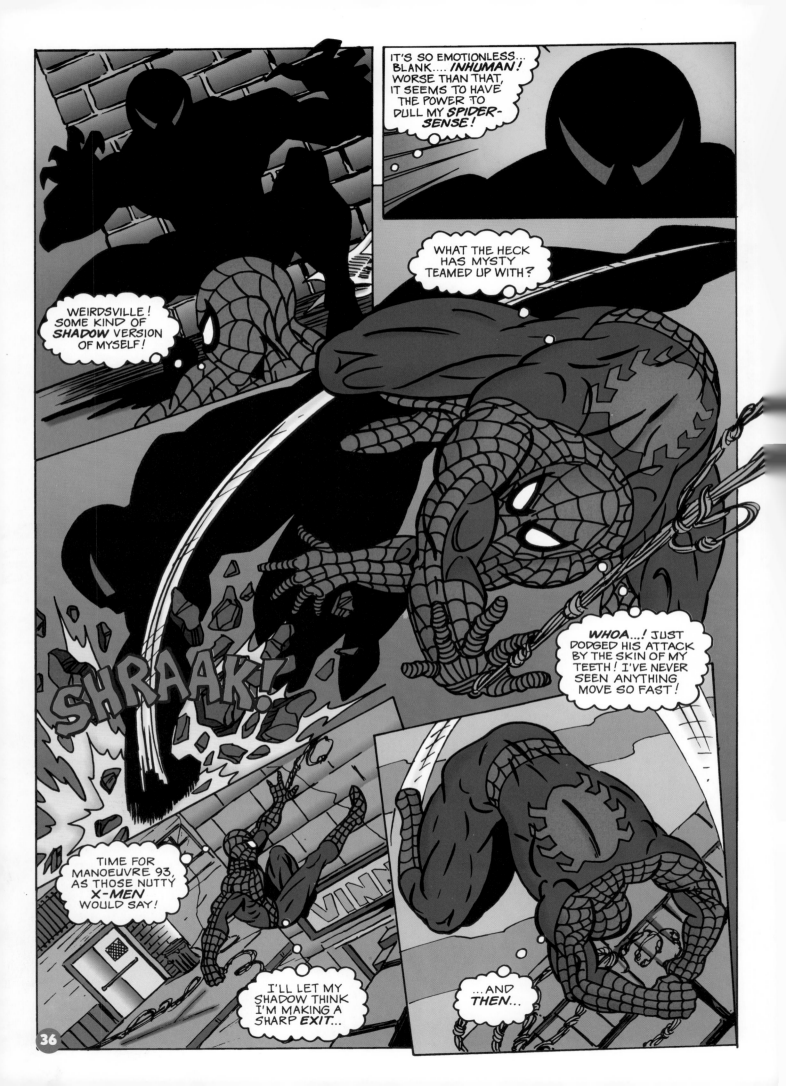

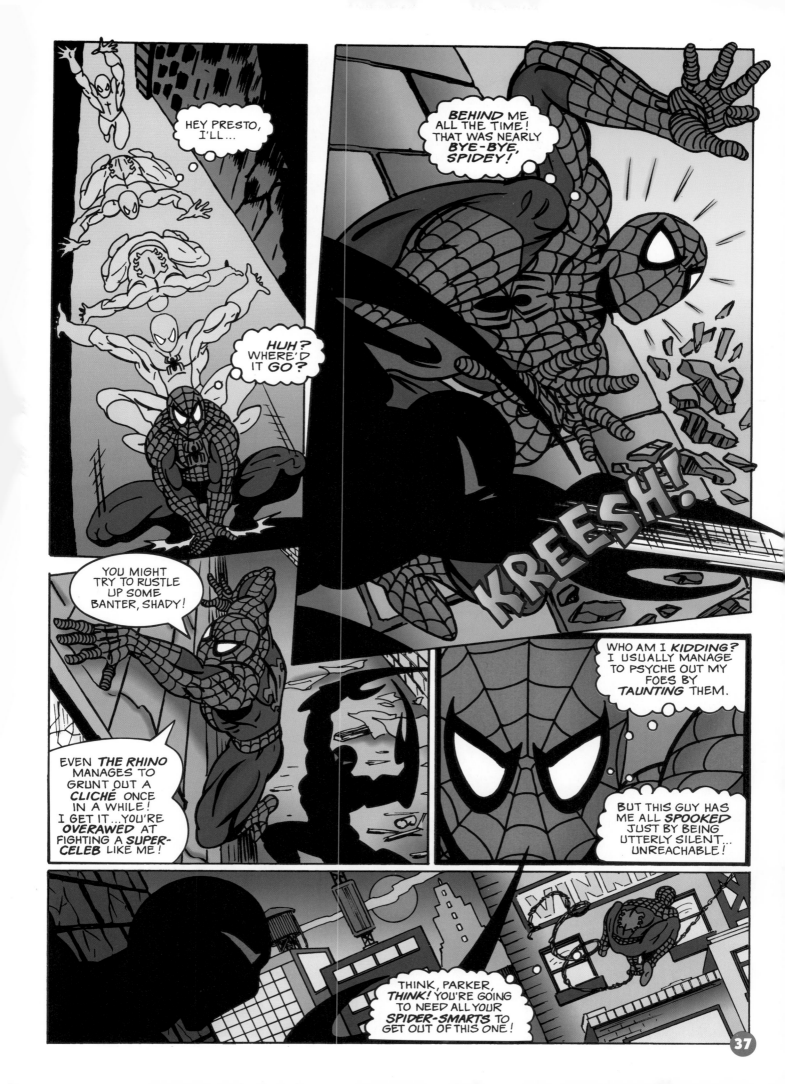

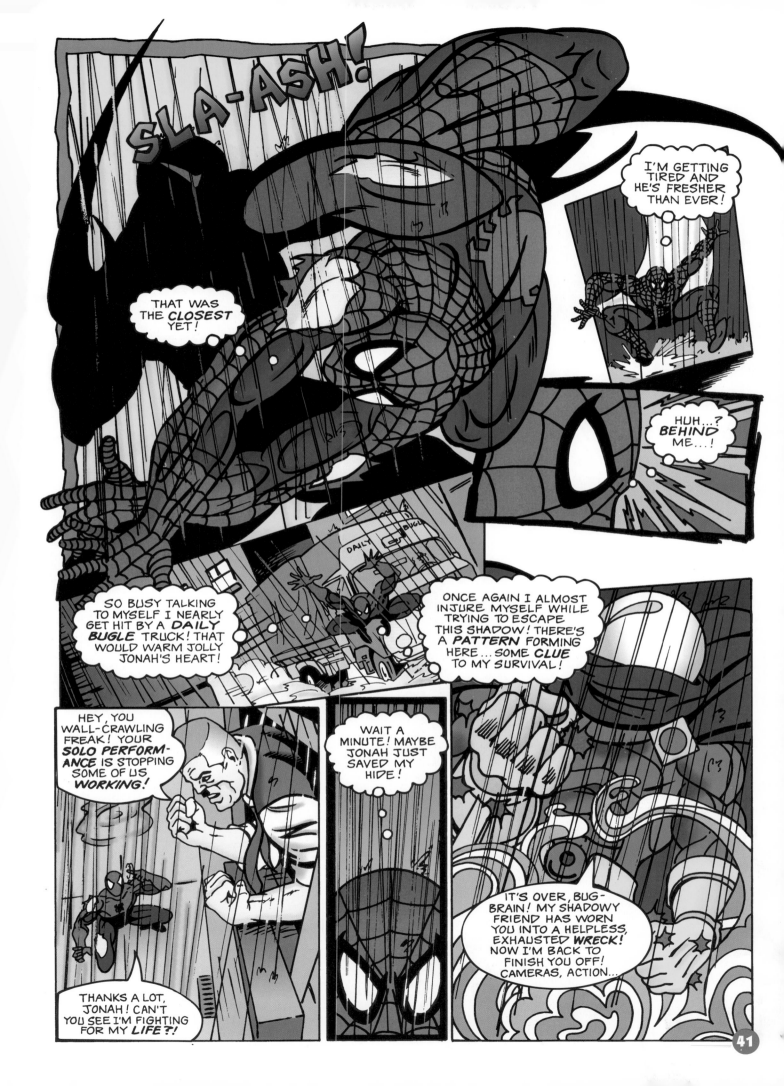

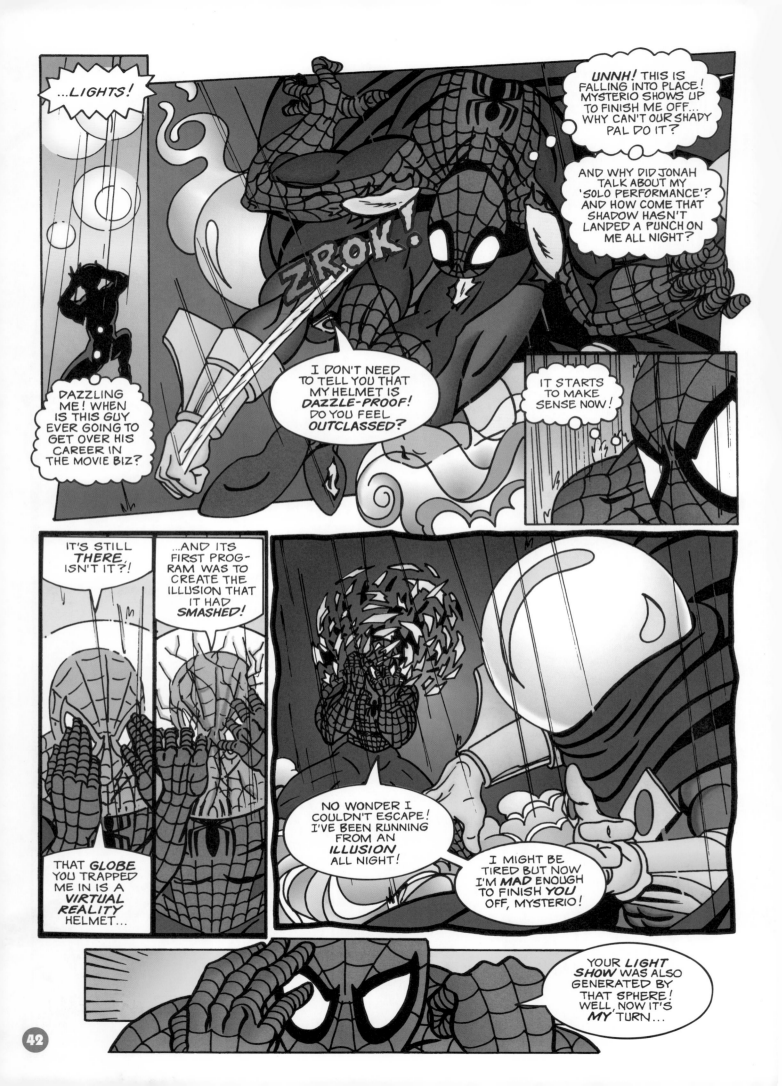

...LIGHTS!

ZROK!

UNNH! THIS IS FALLING INTO PLACE! MYSTERIO SHOWS UP TO FINISH ME OFF... WHY CAN'T OUR SHADY PAL DO IT?

AND WHY DID JONAH TALK ABOUT MY 'SOLO PERFORMANCE'? AND HOW COME THAT SHADOW HASN'T LANDED A PUNCH ON ME ALL NIGHT?

DAZZLING ME! WHEN IS THIS GUY EVER GOING TO GET OVER HIS CAREER IN THE MOVIE BIZ?

I DON'T NEED TO TELL YOU THAT MY HELMET IS DAZZLE-PROOF! DO YOU FEEL OUTCLASSED?

IT STARTS TO MAKE SENSE NOW!

IT'S STILL THERE, ISN'T IT?!

...AND ITS FIRST PROGRAM WAS TO CREATE THE ILLUSION THAT IT HAD SMASHED!

THAT GLOBE YOU TRAPPED ME IN IS A VIRTUAL REALITY HELMET...

NO WONDER I COULDN'T ESCAPE! I'VE BEEN RUNNING FROM AN ILLUSION ALL NIGHT!

I MIGHT BE TIRED BUT NOW I'M MAD ENOUGH TO FINISH YOU OFF, MYSTERIO!

YOUR LIGHT SHOW WAS ALSO GENERATED BY THAT SPHERE! WELL, NOW IT'S MY TURN...

THAT'S FOR YOUR CUTE *FISHBOWL* TRICK!

THAT'S FOR MAKING ME PLAY 'ME AND MY SHADOW'!

AND *THAT'S* FOR MY *SPAGHETTI CARBONARA!*

THRACK!

I THINK YOU GUYS HAVE BEEN LOOKING FOR THIS LIVING LEGEND!

LUCKY I REMEMBERED THAT STASH OF WEB FLUID I HID AT THE DAILY BUGLE BUILDING.

SPAGHETTI CARBONARA...?

HEY, IT'S *MYSTERIO!* THANKS, SPIDEY!

ANY CHANCE OF A *FREE* SNACK, PAL? I'VE BEEN SAVING THE AMERICAN WAY OF LIFE ALL NIGHT!

HUH! I BET YOU'VE BEEN ON A *DATE!* HAVE A BITE ANYWAY... YOU LOOK *WASTED,* YOU POOR SCHMUCK!

HERE, JONAH. WE HAVE TO LOOK AFTER OUR *WORK-AHOLICS!* WRITE SOMETHING NICE ABOUT ME SOMETIME IN YOUR PAPER!

YOU'RE GIVING *ME* A DOUGHNUT AND COFFEE?! NOW I'VE SEEN *EVERYTHING!*

4 A.M. ...

SO YOU MIGHT BE A *LITTLE* LATE, MR. PARKER?!

WELL, I'LL SHOW YOU WHAT LATE *REALLY* MEANS THE NEXT TIME YOU ASK ME OUT!

I SUPPOSE I SHOULD BE FEELING MY USUAL *HARD LUCK* SELF... BUT AFTER TONIGHT, I JUST FEEL KIND OF LUCKY TO BE *ALIVE!* EVEN THAT BURNT CARBONARA SMELLS GOOD!

MAYBE I'M JUST ONE MIXED-UP GUY IN LOVE WITH LIFE! OR PERHAPS I'M AS *FLAKY* AS JOLLY JONAH THINKS I AM!

THE END

Animating SPIDER-MAN

Meeting the creative team behind the SPIDER-MAN animated show

The offices of Marvel Films Animation in Los Angeles are the headquarters of the hit animated TV series, *Spider-Man*. Producer/story editor John Semper is clearly delighted to be working on the show. "I have

the greatest job in the world," he revealed in Marvel Age magazine in June 1994. "I can take the entire Spider-Man saga and pick and choose that which I think is exciting enough to bring to the animated screen."

Interviewed in Comics Scene magazine in January 1994, Semper explained that Marvel Films are determined that Spider-Man's character in the television show should be true to the way he is depicted in the comic books: "I wanted to do a show that took all of the comic book's elements, scrambled them up and kept them relatively the same, but different!

"Our Peter Parker is a teenager who's only had his spider powers for a few years. When Spider-Man's fighting these super villains...what makes it unique is that he also brings with him the problems created when he was plain old Peter Parker. All of those disappointments and frustrations are what make his battles interesting."

Art Director Dennis Venizelos, speaking in Comics Scene in March 1994, agreed with this view: "Spidey himself is just a normal guy who was bitten by a spider. He still has all the problems of everyday life. The regular characters are important because the whole show is about them and Spidey. Basically, they're everyday people - not super people. Even the villains are everyday people whose lives have gone awry."

Dynamic Direction

"We make Spider-Man more spider-like than you've seen him in the past," promises Venizelos. "He's not strolling down streets, he's climbing and rappelling off walls, doing all the somersaults, swinging and fun stuff. Of all the characters, Spidey is the most fun to draw. He's the one you can put in all kinds of positions and he'll still look good."

In order to capture the excitement of Spider-Man's web-swinging adventures, Venizelos places great emphasis on the pacing of the show. Constant movement is one of the keys to the amazing arachnid. "There's a lot of action: in one show, Spider-Man and Doctor Octopus fight in a rocket booster assembly plant!"

Spidey's spider-sense, which warns him of impending danger, caused some problems in the early planning stages. As John Semper explained, it was difficult to know how best to represent it in an animated style: " We do it accurately. We use it as a 'sense', like intuition. If someone is intending direct harm on Spidey, his spider-sense goes off. There's hardly an episode in which his spider-sense isn't used in one way or another."

From time to time, Marvel Films Animation make small modifications with the characters, though any changes have to be approved first by Marvel's comic division. Spider-Man's amazing webbing was a case in point.

"It always bothered me that a science student could invent this brilliant web fluid," Semper told Comics Scene. "I thought 'Wouldn't it be cool if the spider that gave him his powers also enabled him to come up with this formula?' It was transferred by the spider bite. Because a spider inherently knows how to make this stuff, so does Spider-Man."

The story of Spider-Man's origin, where Peter Parker gains his powers after being bitten by a radioactive spider, is told over the course of two episodes, in the form of flashback sequences. "We don't do an 'origin episode' because it's one of those things we've all seen a lot," says Semper. "In the second season, we find out aspects of the origin we've never known before."

The close involvement of Spider-Man's co-creator Stan Lee further ensures the faithfulness of Spidey's depiction in the show. For John Semper, this is one of the highlights of working on *Spider-Man*. "I'm a gigantic

Stan Lee fan," he enthuses. "He personally asked me to do this show. There are milestones in your life where you think 'Gee, maybe I've actually arrived on some level.' When Stan said 'I would really like you to work on Spider-Man,' that was one of those milestones."

Stan Lee himself, as executive producer and chairman of Marvel Films, is keen to ensure that his

character is handled correctly: "We're trying to take as many qualities as possible from the Spider-Man books and put them in the show. That, of course, includes the angst, the humour...everything that we might do here is in the comic book itself."

"Stan is extremely supportive and critical," declares Semper. "I'm messing with his creation and he doesn't let me forget it!"

Moving Pictures

The animation is produced in Japan by a huge team of highly skilled animators and background artists. Hundreds of talented illustrators create the incredible 15,000 to 20,000 cels needed to bring each episode to life. The whole process requires 15 to 20 weeks to complete an episode.

"Almost all of the stories start with me," explained John Semper in Comics Scene. "I never thought I would say this, but 65 episodes aren't enough! I just ate up 13 episodes essentially doing one story. We have drama, action, guest stars and I could easily have done twice as much - there's not enough room. We're cramming so much good stuff into the series."

Villainous Guests

There is certainly no danger of Spider-Man having time on his hands, with the rich assortment of super villains lining up to put him through his paces. Dennis Venizelos is keen to make sure that full use is made of Spidey's colourful supporting cast of classic villains. "Spider-Man is one show that definitely 'brings on the bad guys'. We have 'em all...Doctor Octopus, the Shocker, Hydro Man, the Chameleon, Kraven the Hunter. We try to update them a little bit. With the Vulture, we added more youth to him rather than have the old person he used to be [in the comics]."

Adds John Semper: "We're going to do the whole Green Goblin story at some point...the Green Goblin is a very important part of the Spider-Man saga. We have

Norman Osborn before he becomes the Green Goblin, and his son Harry - Peter Parker's best friend. It's one thing to have a superhero fight a guy flying around on a bat jet throwing pumpkin bombs, but it's another thing when the guy throwing the bombs happens to be the insane father of the superhero's best friend in private life. If we don't have those kinds of complications, then we don't really have Spider-Man.

"We're gonna throw some surprises at you. We have the Hobgoblin, but you won't know who it is. You'll just have to watch the show," he smiles.

Semper reveals that there are also plans in store for *Spider-Man* to feature guest appearances from other Marvel superheroes. "I want to do one [episode] with Doctor Strange! Spider-Man will meet the X-Men and all kinds of other Marvel characters."

The Big Apple

One aspect of the comics that is definitely incorporated into the animated show is the geographical setting. Spider-Man has always been based in New York, and by setting the action against a realistic backdrop, the stories themselves become more believable, as Dennis Venizelos explains: "We actually take positions of real places in New York. For example, the George Washington Bridge is where the space shuttle crashes with Venom in it. Peter Parker lives in the same place he does in the comics (Forest

Hills), a sleepy neighbourhood with quiet residential streets."

And what of some of New York's most celebrated landmarks...the Statue of Liberty, for example?

"Although we haven't used the Statue of Liberty yet, we will," confirms Venizelos, "and the World Trade Center is always in the background in the city shots. Using New York, we've tried to get a more photo-realistic look. We're trying to do a live-action show in animation."

All this requires an enormous amount of painstaking research, with background artists working from photographs and reference books and consulting with maps to check for geographical accuracy. Supervising Producer Bob Richardson explained in June 1994's Marvel Age magazine: "It's a challenge getting all the places right. Our feeling is, let's populate this city, let's make it so that when you're down at street level, there are crowds of people and cars going by. And then the picture moves up the side of a building, and there's Spider-Man."

When Spider-Man swings high above the streets of New York, says Venizelos, the intention is for viewers to share in that experience, to feel as if they're actually swinging up there with Spidey himself: "We want to give it that vertigo look - you're actually up high, looking down, and we have computer shots to give you a dizzy feeling."

Voicing The Characters

An area of the show where the creative team are not able to draw on the influence of the comic books is the sound. Bringing the characters vividly to life not only depends on the skill of the animators and artists, it also falls to the actors whose vocal talents are responsible for the characterisations.

"Chris Barnes is great as Peter Parker and Spidey," says producer Semper proudly. "He's a talented guy."

Peter Parker's vivacious girlfriend Mary Jane Watson is voiced by Saratoga Ballantine, who spoke of her affection for the character in the March 1994 issue of Comics Scene: "Mary Jane is terrific; she just wants to

be a performer. I would want to be her best friend. She is bright, funny and cute."

She is equally enthusiastic for her co-star Chris Barnes. "Chris is an amazing person. He's very focused and confident. He makes Peter Parker come alive. On the show, I don't know that he's Spider-Man, but I'm starting to get suspicious. As Mary Jane, I know Peter Parker and I've met Spider-Man too, but I don't know they're the same person...yet."

John Semper sees Mary Jane as being very likeable. "[She's] an interesting character and a strong woman. She's a college student and aspiring actress/model. We even do her first appearance, the 'Face it, Tiger - you just hit the jackpot' scene."

"It's a cute and famous thing that Mary Jane calls people 'Tiger'," laughs Saratoga Ballantine. "I find I'm calling everybody 'Tiger' now, so life is imitating art!"

Dennis Venizelos explains that the voice of Peter's doting Aunt May was decided upon before her visual appearance had been finalised: "We looked at certain voices to see what she sounded like before we designed her. From there, we developed the

character. She has to have a very soft, nice voice to give her that motherly image. Aunt May was redesigned because she has to raise Peter and he's rambunctious, and she couldn't do it if she was too frail."

Spider-Man's eternal adversary, the Daily Bugle's irascible publisher J. Jonah Jameson, is voiced by respected American actor Ed Asner.

"When you have Ed Asner playing J. Jonah Jameson," declares Semper, "you have to make him a real human being, otherwise it's a waste of Ed Asner. We have a zillion cartoon voices out there who could yell 'Parker!' but when you have Ed Asner you have to give him some drama."

In the comic version, J. Jonah Jameson's hatred of Spider-Man stems from his secret envy of the amazing web-swinger but John Semper felt this didn't really explain Jameson's antagonism towards Spidey. "The jealousy thing always played pretty two-dimensional to me. I talked it over with Stan Lee and he said 'You know, I never thought of a better reason.' I've given him a real reason for not liking Spider-Man. We reveal that J. Jonah has a reason in his past for not liking men who wear masks and take the law into their own hands. [It] makes Jonah a credible character, not a guy who stupidly and unmotivatedly hates Spider-Man. [He's] really on a mission - he feels vigilantes are a problem.

"There's a lot of interesting interplay between him and Spider-Man. There's fun stuff, too, like webbing Jameson to the ceiling! It's all there."

John Semper is very happy indeed with the team of voice actors which has been assembled to breathe life into the Spider-Man characters.

"Saratoga Ballantine is sweet and incredibly talented. I'm having fun writing for her. Mark Hamill gives a tremendous performance as the Hobgoblin. I'm very happy to have Mark on this show," says Semper, a feeling echoed by Saratoga Ballantine: "Mark Hamill [is] incredible. His Hobgoblin is really great; Mark is such a performer that even a little line becomes a mini-series. He's so rich and full of character."

"We have Roscoe Lee Browne as the Kingpin," adds John Semper. "The Kingpin is an extremely important character to us, because he is the major villain. He turns up in most of our episodes, if not all of them. We've made him into a bigger, more sinister and global character."

The success of Spider-Man has led to many famous actors expressing a desire to lend their vocal talents to the show.

"We've had some really cool people," says Ballantine. "Everybody wants to do the show and it's attracting a great deal of celebrity interest. With your voice, you can do a lot more things than you can with your face. You can manipulate it all kinds of ways. It's a much more liberating thing."

We'll leave the final word to producer/story editor John Semper: "Everybody better watch, because we can do anything! As long as I'm doing this show, it's gonna be one surprise after another, no holds barred."

Hang on to your webs, spider-fans!

Deadly Night Shift

Story: James Hill Art: Adrian Phillips

Peter Parker yawned and rubbed his eyes. He'd been sitting in the examination room for less than an hour but already he was struggling to stay awake. This wasn't the way it was supposed to be in exam week, he thought. He had always believed that if he attended lectures and studied hard, he would do all right. He was, after all, a physics genius. Lots of average students at ESU were going to sail through their exams with flying colours, why shouldn't he?

But Peter Parker was different. Peter Parker was secretly the amazing Spider-Man. Every night, suspended from impossibly strong webs of his own creation, he swung out across the city to fight crime. Last night had been particularly gruelling. Three jewellery heists, a bank raid and a battle between competing mob gangs had meant that Spider-Man had been run ragged. He'd returned home as the sun was rising over the city and immersed himself in study for another five hours. By the time his physics exam started, Peter could quite happily have curled up in bed for a week.

"Pens down, please!"

At the sound of Professor Hartmann's voice, Peter's eyes blinked open. "Huh? Wh-what..?" he muttered groggily, trying to regain his composure. "Time's up already?"

The exam papers were collected and the students filed out into a bright, sunny afternoon.

"Hey, Pete!" called Harry Osborn, racing over to join his flatmate on the steps of the university's main science building. "Boy, you look wrecked! I keep tellin' ya...all work and no play just ain't natural for a guy your age!"

"You're right, Harry," said Peter wearily. "I'm heading home for one hot date...with a scalding shower and bed!"

That night, Spider-Man looked out across New York. Few others had seen the city like this -– a luxurious velvet blanket studded with jewels of light. And it was upside down! All at once, every muscle in his body tensed, each nerve screaming for him to act. It was his spider-sense, warning him of imminent danger. Spider-Man scanned the street below but all he could see was a small construction team working overtime to complete the building of a new office block.

Suddenly...incredibly...the office building began to fall in on itself, engulfing the construction workers in a deadly cascade of dirt, bricks and steel!

Spider-Man propelled himself down towards street level. Glutinous strands of webbing snaked from his web-shooters, snagging a lamp-post. At spectacular speed, Spider-Man swung past the disintegrating building, grabbing two workers and depositing them safely on the opposite pavement. Within seconds, he was back amidst the rubble of the office building and through the cloying dust he could just about make out a huge silhouetted figure.

"Man! Who is that?! Even his muscles have got muscles!" he gasped. "Whoever he is, I have a hunch he's behind this!"

The web-slinger leapt after the mysterious giant but before he could fire his webbing, the looming creature turned and came charging towards him. Swatted away with a backwards flick of the fiend's hand, Spider-Man went crashing into a pile of masonry. In the time it took him to get to his feet again, the sinister figure had disappeared, his escape route hidden by the billowing dust cloud.

"Great..." thought Spidey, rubbing his head.

Peter Parker's electronic alarm clock pulsed into life at precisely 7.15 a.m., piercing the silence of his bedroom until a glob of webbing struck the snooze button.

Spider-Man dropped lithely through the skylight. "Hey, keep it down," he shushed, aware that Harry would still be asleep in the next room.

Peter yawned. The destruction of the office block had been followed by further devastating acts of vandalism. A train had been derailed, an all-night cinema had been wrecked and a vault had been torn from a high street bank and abandoned in the centre of a busy highway.

At first, the mayhem had seemed to be without a purpose, utterly mindless. But now Peter was beginning detect a pattern. Each act of vandalism had occurre somewhere along the route of one of Spider-Man's regu patrols.

"It's as if that guy knew just where I'd be and wher he mused. "If he's trying to tire me out, it's sure working. B there's got to be more to it than that..."

The next night followed the pattern of the previous evening, with Spider-Man constantly one step behind h mysterious adversary. Still, though he arrived at th scenes of destruction some time after the hulking brute ha disappeared into the shadows, he had managed to save mar lives. And tonight? So far, tonight had been peaceful and th amazing arachnid was swinging home to prepare for his fin exam in the morning.

"Man, I can't believe I'm finally gonna grab som shut-eye!" he yawned. It was only then that he saw it – sudden blur of movement ahead and to the right, as something was about to intercept his path.

In the darkness, something collided with him. Before he could gather his wits he found himself tumbling head ove heels towards the streets far below.

"Web-line broken," he groaned. "Caught me of guard..."

"Petey! Fancy bumping into you!" The voice was deep and booming, instantly recognisable.

"Venom!" Spider-Man spat out the word. Above him, perched atop a towering building, sat the hunched form of the most unpredictable villain he'd ever faced, glowering madly.

As he fell, Spider-Man hastily fired his web-shooters, creating a taut, trampoline-like tapestry beneath him. Hitting the trampoline, he was propelled back into the air, landing lightly on the side of the building. Moments later, Venom had slithered down to join him.

"Now, Peter," sneered the sinister being, "we can't have you going home to bed while there's still work to be done, can we?"

"You won't find me sleeping on this job, Brock," promised Spider-Man as he fired a thick stream of webbing at his leering foe. Venom shredded it with a super-speed slash of his hand.

Spider-Man took a deep breath. This wasn't going to be easy. Venom was actually an alien symbiote bonded to reporter Eddie Brock. Together they had formed a deadly creature with powers that mimicked Spider-Man's own. In addition, they knew his secrets – the routes of his patrols, his real identity, his friends and where they lived. Since their first encounter, Venom had returned time and again to taunt the web-spinner.

"What are you doing, Brock?" demanded Spider-Man. "Why have me racing around after you every night? Are you trying to tire me out? That's lame, even for you!"

Venom hissed insanely. "What better way to ruin Peter Parker than to make sure he fails all his exams? What will dear old Aunt May say? Your friends? You'll be a laughing stock! Then – and only then – will we finally destroy you!"

With a joyless cackle, Venom launched himself into the night. Spider-Man had no choice but to follow. For long hours, the pair raced across town on their web-lines.

Dawn was finally breaking as Spider-Man and Venom approached a road running parallel to the Hudson River.

"Up and at 'em, New York! It's a beautiful morning!" sang Venom, as he crashed onto the roof of a delivery truck. It careered wildly, but Venom hung on effortlessly, digging his fingers into the vehicle as if it were made of butter.

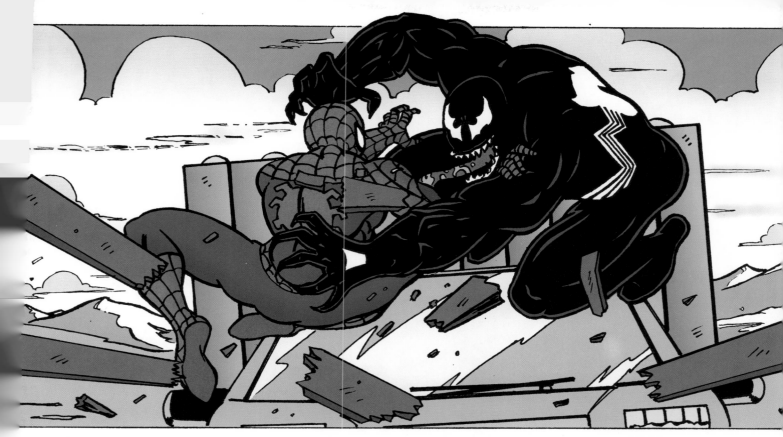

"Hey! Wh-what's goin' on?" stammered the truck driver.

Venom's face appeared at the window. "You've picked up a new passenger!" he announced with glee.

"Hey, Brock-baby! Didn't your folks warn you hitchhiking could be dangerous?" called Spider-Man, landing on the truck beside Venom and pinning him to the roof. There, the deadly adversaries locked together, pushing and straining against each other in a seemingly perfect stalemate.

"Limbs aching yet, Spider-Man?" asked Venom. "Eyes feeling heavy? You can't keep this up for much longer!"

Venom lashed out against Spider-Man, and the sudden shift of weight on top of the truck caused it to lurch sideways. Crashing through a brittle wooden barrier, it fell towards the icy waters of the Hudson River.

"Oops! Gotta fly!" declared Venom, leaping out of the way of danger.

Wrenching the cab door from its hinges, Spider-Man dragged the driver clear of the truck just as it plunged into the grey depths of the river, taking its boxed cargo down with it.

Setting the shaken trucker safely down at the side of the road, Spider-Man caught sight of Venom entering a tunnel that took traffic beneath the river. Bouncing from car roof to car roof, the web-spinner landed inside the darkened tunnel which was already choked with early morning commuter traffic, shrill horns echoing in the confined space. Spider-Man paused to catch his breath. Venom had been right...he was tiring, the lack of sleep finally taking its toll. Fighting against his exhaustion, Spidey peered into the dank gloom for a sign of his enemy.

"Outta the way, ugly!"

Spider-Man turned at the sound of the gruff voice. Unbelievably, there stood Venom, frozen in the headlights of an angry motorist.

"Oh, boy!" gasped Spider-Man. "Unless I act quickly, that guy's going to experience road rage – Venom-style!"

The wall-crawler tensed to leap, but then paused. He could see that Venom had made no move towards the irate motorist. In fact, the slavering giant was rooted to the spot. The reality of the situation became clear. Venom was trapped!

The alien symbiote that had possessed Eddie Brock had only one weakness – sound. And here, deep within the tunnel, where the amplified cacophony of blaring horns and revving engines had taken on an eerie distorted quality, Venom was under attack, racked with searing pain. Finally, his hands pressed to the sides of his head in an effort to block out the overwhelming noise, Venom let out a agonised scream and slumped slowly to his knees, defeated. The alien symbiote, overpowered by the sonic onslaught, drained limply away from its host, draping itself over Eddie Brock's unconscious body like a seemingly lifeless black shadow.

Spider-Man approached the comatose figure. "Okay, folks," he said. "Show's over. I'll take care of this guy."

Slumped on the couch in his apartment, Peter Parker was exhausted. He had delivered Brock and the symbiote to Reed Richards, the leader of the Fantastic Four, for study and safe-keeping. But by the time Spider-Man had helped secure Brock inside a sonic field generator, Peter Parker had missed the start of his exam. Venom had succeeded in wrecking Peter's life, after all.

Peter's reverie was broken by Harry Osborn bursting excitedly through the door.

"Harry, shouldn't you be sitting an exam?" asked Peter.

"Haven't you heard?" laughed Harry. "The exams have been cancelled! The delivery truck carrying the papers was wrecked in a battle between Spider-Man and Venom and everything ended up at the bottom of the Hudson. We've got a whole week before the new papers can be set!"

Peter tried his best, but he couldn't suppress his laughter.

"What are you gonna do with your free time, Pete?" asked Harry. "Some of us are going camping. Fancy coming along with us?"

"Naw," replied Peter. "Thanks, Harry, but I think I'll catch up on some sleep."

"Hey, what a full and eventful life you live!" joked Harry. "How do you manage it?"

"Harry, old pal," smiled Peter, stretching, "you don't know the half of it..."

THE BERSERKER MACHINE!

I CAN'T BELIEVE IT'S COME TO THIS. *PETER PARKER*, AKA YOUR FRIENDLY NEIGHBOURHOOD *SPIDER-MAN*...

...HAVING TO TAKE PHOTOS OF *OSCORP'S* LATEST INVENTION JUST TO PAY THE RENT! MAYBE I SHOULD JOIN *THE AVENGERS* OR SOMETHING...

"AT LEAST I CAN KEEP AN EYE ON *OSBORN*."

"AS THE *GREEN GOBLIN*, HE PROVED TO BE ONE OF MY MOST DANGEROUS ENEMIES!"

"THOUGH WHEN HE REGAINED HIS SANITY, HE DIDN'T EVEN REMEMBER BEING THE GREEN GOBLIN."

...AND SO THE *SOMNAMBULATOR* WILL EASE THE MORE AGGRESSIVE TENDENCIES OF *UNSTABLE PERSONALITIES*...

...AS THE GOOD PROFESSOR WILL NOW DEMONSTRATE.

A *RELAXATION MACHINE?!* FOR THIS, I'M MISSING A DATE WITH *MARY JANE*... SHEESH! UH-OH... *SPIDER-SENSE* IS GOING CRAZY!

50

Script: Alan Cowsill Art: Jon Rushby and Brian Williamson Lettering: Peter Nicholls

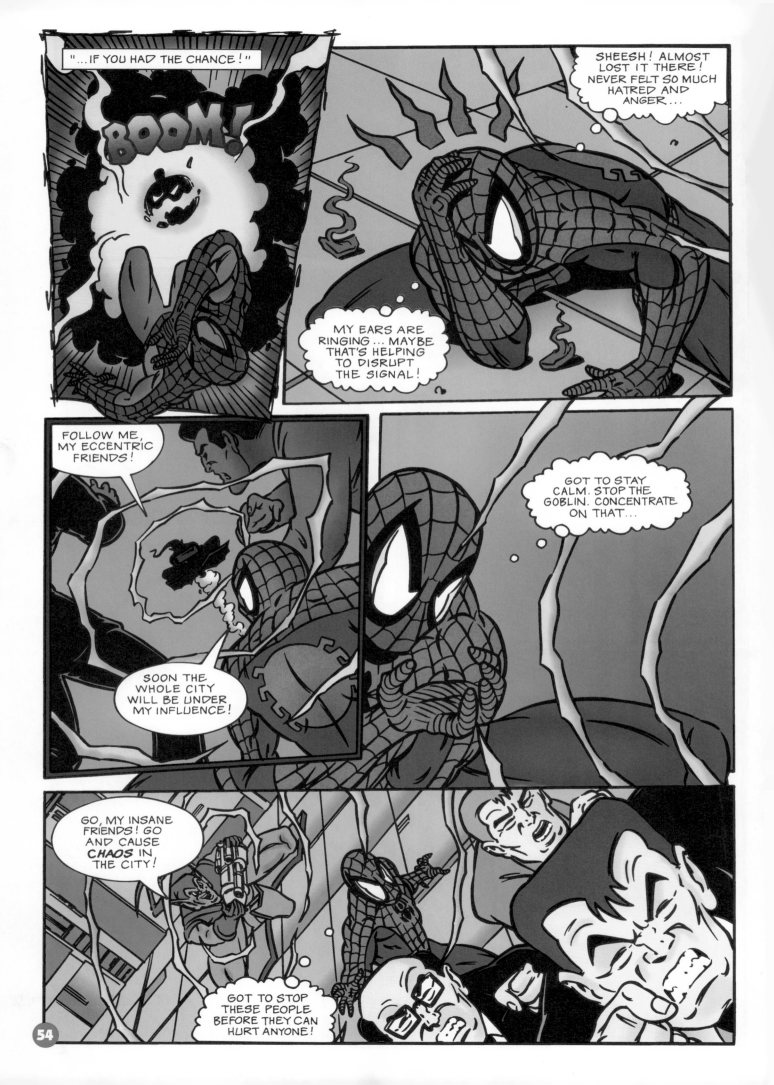